CONTENT[S]

Retold by Denys Johnson-Davies
Illustrated by Nessim Girgis

The British Council, Cairo

GOHA AND THE CHILDREN'S PARTY

Once Goha was walking down the street, minding his own business. Suddenly some children started to throw stones at him. He didn't know whether to run away or to throw stones back at them. Instead, he shouted at them: "If you stop doing that I'll tell you something you'd like to hear."

"Tell us," said the children. "What is it?"

"The prince is giving a big party and everyone is invited. They say there will be cream cakes."

The children immediately stopped throwing stones and ran off to the prince's palace.

2

Goha watched them as they ran down the street. Then, suddenly, he followed after them as quickly as his legs would carry him. "After all," he told himself, "it might just be true."

GOHA AND HIS LAMP

Goha was sitting in the café one day, telling people that he could see in the dark.

"If you can really see in the dark," said one of those sitting with him, "why do you always carry with you a lamp at night?"

"Oh that," said Goha, "is just so that people won't bump into me."

GOHA WORKS AS A PORTER

It was a difficult time for Goha and he had to work as a porter. A man asked him to carry a basket which contained some little glass bottles. The man told him that on the way he would teach him three things which would always be useful to him.

Goha and the owner of the bottles set off through the lanes of the village. Goha was struggling under the weight of the heavy basket. When they had walked a little, Goha wanted to have a rest. He asked the man to tell him one of the three things he had mentioned.

So the man sat down on the steps of a shop beside Goha and said: "He who says to you that hunger is better than a full stomach, don't believe him."

Goha nodded his head, then stood up and picked up the basket of bottles.

After a while Goha needed to sit down again. He asked the man to tell him the second of the three things. So the man said: "He who says to you that walking is better than riding, don't believe him."

Again Goha nodded, then stood up and picked up the load of bottles. The man walked on to show him the way to his house.

Finally they arrived at the house. The sweat was pouring off Goha's body. Then Goha said to the man: "Now tell me the third thing you promised me." The man answered him:

"He who says to you that you will get some money for carrying this basket of bottles, don't believe him."

At this, Goha threw down the basket and shouted: "And he who says to you that there are any unbroken bottles in this basket, don't believe him!"

GOHA'S DONKEY CONTRADICTS HIM

One day Goha's neighbour came to him and asked if he could borrow his donkey. However, Goha never liked to lend his donkey to anyone, because he was not sure how others would treat it. People were often cruel to their donkeys, and they might be even more cruel to a donkey that did not belong to them.

"I am sorry," said Goha to his neighbour, "but I have already lent my donkey to a friend of mine, who has taken it to another village."

As soon as the words had left Goha's mouth the donkey brayed loudly in the stable nearby.

The neighbour looked at Goha angrily and said: "How can you say that the donkey is not here? I can hear it braying in its stable."

Goha turned to the man and shook his head sadly:

"I am surprised that someone like you would believe a donkey rather than this white-haired Sheikh who has been your neighbour for so many years."

GOHA IS GIVEN A RABBIT

A peasant came to Goha's house and gave him a rabbit as a present. Goha was delighted and gave the rabbit to his wife. He asked her to prepare a stew from the rabbit and invited the peasant to share the meal with him.

The following week the same peasant came to Goha's house and reminded him that he was the man who had brought the rabbit. Goha welcomed the peasant warmly and once again asked him to share his meal.

A few weeks later four peasants came and knocked at the door of Goha's house. He asked who they were, and they told him they were the neighbours of the man who had brought Goha the rabbit. Goha welcomed them and asked his wife to prepare food for the four of them.

8

Then, several weeks later, more peasants knocked at Goha's door. This time they said that they were neighbours of the four neighbours of the man who had given him the rabbit. Again Goha welcomed them into his house and asked his wife to fill a large dish with hot water. He placed this in front of his visitors. They were amazed that the dish contained only water.

"And what is this, O Sheikh Goha?" they asked.

"This," Goha answered, "is the soup of the soup of the rabbit, O neighbours of the neighbours of the man who gave it to me."

GOHA THE SMUGGLER

Goha once lived on the border between two countries. He often used to travel from one country to the other. Always, when he passed through the border, he was riding a donkey with two or three other donkeys with him. All the donkeys had baskets tied to their sides. The guards at the border were sure that Goha was smuggling something. They always searched the baskets but never found anything valuable in them.

After many years of travelling through with his donkeys and their baskets, Goha went to live in a faraway country. It was

clear from his clothes and the way he lived that he had
become a rich man - no doubt from all the smuggling.
By chance, one of the border guards who had known Goha
and had often searched the baskets on his donkeys came
across Goha in the faraway country.

"Tell me, Goha, we always knew you were smuggling
something but we could never catch you. Tell me, what was it
that you were smuggling?"

"Donkeys!" answered Goha.

GOHA GOES TO HUNT BEARS

Goha used often to go to the court of the prince who ruled over the town where he lived. The prince used to enjoy Goha's amusing conversation. One day the prince decided to go into the mountains to hunt bears and he asked Goha to go with him. Although Goha was shaking with fear at the thought of hunting bears, he could not refuse the prince's invitation. When Goha returned safely from the hunt, his friends were curious to know how things had gone.

"Excellently," said Goha.

"How many bears did you kill?"

"None," answered Goha.

"How many bears did you chase through the mountains?"

"None," answered Goha.

"How many bears did you see?" asked his friends.

"None," answered Goha again.

"How, then, can you say that it was an excellent hunt when you didn't even see a bear?"

"When you are hunting bears," Goha answered them, "none is the best number."

GOHA NEEDS A DRINK OF WATER

Goha travelled to another town and had to stay the night at the local hotel. When the hotel-keeper welcomed him, he said: "Now, if during the night you need anything, all you have to do is call out for it."

During the night Goha felt very thirsty and called out for a glass of water, but no-one came.

Then Goha began shouting at the top of his voice: "Fire! Fire!" Immediately, the hotel-keeper rushed into Goha's room with a bucket of water. "Where's the fire?" he asked.

"Here," said Goha, pointing to his mouth

GOHA'S WAY OF COUNTING MADMEN

The chief official from the town council came to Goha. He told Goha that he wished to know how many madmen there were in the town. He asked him if he would count them. Goha thought about this and said: "To be honest, there are so many madmen in our town that it would take a long time to count them all. Do you know the total population of our town?"

"Of course we do," said the chief official.

"Then it would be easier for me to count those few people in our town who are *not* mad. Then I can take that number from the total population and so I can discover, without too much effort, the number of madmen that we have."

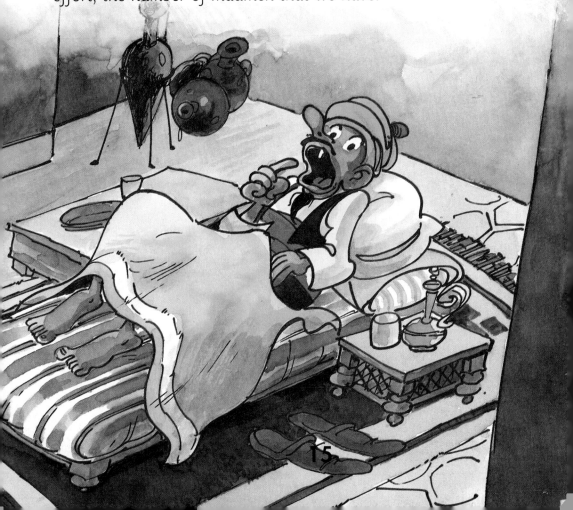

GOHA GIVES A FAIR DECISION

Two brothers had a quarrel, so one of them went to Goha and told him all about the quarrel. He asked Goha for his opinion, for Goha was known by everyone as a very wise man who always gave a fair decision.

After some thought Goha said to him: "You are right and your brother is wrong."

So the first brother, very happy with what Goha had said to him, went off home.

Then the second brother came to Goha and told him about the quarrel and asked for his opinion. After some thought Goha again said:

"You are right and your brother is wrong."

So the second brother also went away happy.

All this time Goha's wife had been listening at the door to what he had said to the two brothers. She came into the room where Goha was sitting and said to him: "How can you say to each of them that he is right and his brother is wrong? That doesn't make sense."

"Don't be angry," Goha said to her. "You're quite right and I'm wrong."

GOHA MAKES HIS CHOICE

Goha was asked: "Who is the greater, the Sultan or the farmer?"

"The farmer of course," answered Goha without hesitation, "because if the farmer doesn't produce food the Sultan will die of starvation."

GOHA COUNTS HIS DONKEYS

Goha decided that he would like to become a merchant. What better than to enter the business of buying and selling donkeys?

He therefore went off to the market where he inspected many donkeys. In the end he bought ten of them. He wanted to take them back home with him, so he climbed onto one of the donkeys and the others walked along in front of him. As he was riding on the back of one of the donkeys, he decided to count them. He was surprised when he found that there were only nine, for he had forgotten to count the one he was riding.

He remembered well that he had bought ten donkeys. Where

18

had the tenth gone? He climbed down from his donkey so as to count them again. This time he found there were ten.

Satisfied, he got back onto the donkey he had been riding. To make sure, he counted the donkeys once again, but found that he had only nine. Then he got off it and counted and found that there were ten. He went on doing this several times, but he could not understand how there were sometimes only nine donkeys and sometimes ten.

At last he said to himself: "It seems that if I walk I gain a donkey, which is better than riding and losing a donkey."

So he walked all the way to his house behind the ten donkeys he had bought at the market.

GOHA LOOKS FOR THE
MISSING DONKEY

The prince of the town in which Goha lived had a favourite donkey. One day it went missing and the prince was very upset. Immediately a lot of people from the town gathered together and went to search for the donkey. They suggested to Goha that he should join them in their search.

Goha had nothing special to do that day, so he went off with the others. He looked here and there in the town for the prince's donkey. As he walked about he sang cheerfully to himself. The people with him were shocked at this and said to him: "This is no way to behave when someone's donkey is lost, especially if that person is the prince."

To this Goha answered: "As long as I am searching for someone else's donkey which is lost, and not mine, I feel cheerful enough to sing!"

GOHA GIVES THANKS TO ALLAH

Goha once lost his donkey. He couldn't find it anywhere. As he went around the town searching for it he kept on saying: "Thanks be to Allah. Thanks be to Allah."

People were surprised to find him giving thanks to Allah when he had lost his donkey. They asked him: "O Goha, why are you saying 'Thanks be to Allah' when you have lost your donkey? Surely that is not something to thank Allah for."

"I am thanking Allah," answered Goha, "because I was not riding it, or I too would be lost."

21

GOHA BUYS MEAT FOR HIS SUPPER

One day Goha thought he would like to have a really good supper, so he bought three kilograms of the best meat and took it to his wife.

"Please cook this meat for our supper tonight," he said to her and left the house.

His wife was a good cook and put the pieces of meat into the oven and prepared some vegetables to go with it, also some rice. While she was doing the cooking her neighbour looked in to see what Goha's wife was cooking for her husband's meal. The two women tried the meat and agreed that it was very tasty.

"Just one more little piece," said the neighbour, and Goha's wife cut two more pieces, one for her and one for her friend. And so they went on eating more and more till suddenly Goha's wife realised they had eaten it all.

When Goha came home for his supper, his wife told him that she was sorry but all that she had were some vegetables and rice.

"And what's happened to the three kilograms of meat I brought you this morning?" asked Goha.

"Oh," she said, "I'm sorry to tell you that, while my back was turned, the cat stole the meat and ate it all up."

Goha gave his wife a look that showed he didn't believe her and went off to look for the cat. When he had found it, he took out a pair of scales and weighed the cat. He found that the cat weighed exactly three kilograms, so he turned to his wife and said:

"O wife, if this is the cat, then where's the meat? And if this is the meat, then where's the cat?"

GOHA AND THE POOR MAN

One day a poor man who was hungry passed by the shop of someone who was grilling meat. The poor man had no money to buy any meat, so he had to satisfy himself by going to a nearby baker and buying a loaf of bread. Then, with his loaf of bread, he went and sat down to eat it near where the meat was being grilled. In this way he had the pleasure of the smell of the meat that was being cooked.

When he had finished eating his loaf of bread, the owner of the shop came out to him and demanded money for smelling the meat. The poor man had no money to pay with, so the owner of the shop took hold of him and led him off to Goha, who had become a judge.

"O wise judge," said the owner of the shop. "This man ate his loaf of bread while he was enjoying the smell of the meat I was grilling. I asked for payment for the smell of the meat but he refused to pay me anything."

Goha thought for a while, then said: "How many piastres are you asking for as the price of the smell of your grilled meat?"

"I am asking for five piastres," said the man.

Then Goha took out of his pocket a five-piastre coin and let it fall with a ringing sound on the table in front of him. "Did you hear the sound that the coin made?" he asked.

"Yes, honourable judge," said the man.

"Then take that sound," said Goha, "as the price of the smell of your grilled meat."

GOHA AND THE TWO ROBBERS

Goha was walking on the edge of the town when he was stopped by two rough-looking men with knives in their belts.

"Unless you hand over to us the money you are carrying we shall kill you," said one of the two robbers, putting his hand on his knife.

Goha was not a brave man and his knees shook when he saw

26

these two fierce men. He felt he would like to sit down for a while, also he wanted time to think.

"Let me just sit down for a while and recover my breath," he asked the two men, so one of them pushed Goha roughly to the ground.

"There is no need for thinking," he shouted at Goha. "Just hand over your money."

While he was on the ground, Goha told the two robbers that they were lucky because he was carrying with him a large amount of money.

When they heard this the two men held out their hands, and their eyes sparkled with greed at the thought of all that money.

"But," Goha told them, "I wish to give the money to just one of you. I therefore suggest that you agree among yourselves as to which of you shall have my money."

The first robber immediately said: "I should have the money, because it was I who first saw you coming."

"No," said the second robber, "it was I who noticed how well dressed you were and that you were certainly carrying with you a big amount of money."

The two robbers then began arguing about which of them deserved to have Goha's money.

Goha told them: "Don't quarrel like that. Come and sit down beside me and decide the matter in a calm and friendly way."

But the two men continued to argue violently, raising their voices as each gave his reasons for being the one to have the money.

At last Goha was able to quieten them down. "I can see," he told them, "that you are not going to agree about this, so I suggest that I give the money to the strongest one of you."

The first robber said: "I am certainly the strongest - I could quickly jump on him and throw him to the ground."

The second robber said: "With a single blow I could break his head."

"Now let each of you show me who is the stronger," said Goha.

The two robbers immediately started to fight. Soon they had forgotten all about Goha as they knocked each other to the ground and the blood flowed from their many wounds.

When each robber had nearly killed the other, Goha quietly got to his feet and left.

GOHA AT THE PUBLIC BATHS

Goha went to the public baths in the town. As usual, he was poorly dressed and so the attendants did not treat him with any respect. He was given only the smallest piece of soap and a little towel that didn't look very clean.

During his time in the baths he was not served tea and cakes like the other customers. In fact, the attendants made it obvious that they would not mind if they never saw him there again.

But when he left the baths Goha gave the two attendants a gold coin each. They were amazed at how this poorly dressed

man, whom they had treated roughly, should suddenly be so generous to them. Perhaps next time, they told themselves, he would be even more generous.

The following week Goha again went to the public baths. This time, despite the fact that he was dressed in the same clothes, he was treated like a king. When he left he handed to each of the attendants the smallest copper coin instead of the gold one he had given them after his first visit.

"This copper coin," explained Goha to the surprised men, "is for the previous visit when I was treated like a beggar. The gold coins I gave you were for this time."

31

GOHA ASKS HIS DONKEY
ITS OPINION

Someone asked Goha if he could borrow his donkey. Goha knew he was a man who had no respect for donkeys and that he often beat them. Goha certainly didn't want to let this happen to his donkey. He therefore said to him: "Wait till I go to consult my donkey about this matter and see what it has to say."

Goha went into his house, stayed some minutes there, then came out and told the man: "I asked my donkey about this, but it did not like the idea. It told me that some of its friends had been beaten by you and it would not like to have the same treatment."

The man looked at Goha disbelievingly but could find nothing to say. He never again asked Goha to lend him his donkey.

GOHA DOESN'T KNOW WHERE
HE'S GOING

Goha was riding his donkey when a dog ran across the road. The donkey was frightened and ran off out of control at top speed.

A passer-by called out to him: "Where are you going to so urgently, Goha?"

"Don't ask me," Goha shouted back. "Ask the donkey!"

GOHA GETS CURED

Goha didn't feel well so his wife called the doctor. The doctor examined Goha and told him to stay in bed for a few days.

His wife told people that her husband was ill and some of them decided to pay him a visit. "Poor Goha," they said, "lying in bed with nothing to do."

So they bought him some grapes and came and sat by his bedside. They talked with him for some time, then they talked among themselves as they ate the grapes they had brought him. Goha began to get tired and bored and wanted to go to sleep. Would they never leave him in peace?

In the end he jumped out of bed and put on his dressing-gown.

"Allah," he told them, "has cured the sick man you were visiting, so you can all go now."

GOHA GIVES HIS SON A LESSON ABOUT PEOPLE

Goha had a son who was always worried about what people would think or say. The boy could never do anything because he was always afraid that people might think him foolish.

Goha wanted to show his son that it was a waste of time to worry about the opinions of others. He therefore saddled his donkey and told his son that he was going to the neighbouring village.

Goha got on his donkey and asked his son to walk behind him. On the way they passed by some people who pointed at Goha and said: "Look at that heartless man who rides his donkey and makes his son walk."

When he heard this, Goha got off the donkey and asked his son to get on, while he himself walked. Again they passed by some people who pointed at the boy and said:

"Just look at that boy who has no manners or respect for the elderly - he rides the donkey and lets his old father walk."

Goha thought about this, so he decided that both he and his son should now ride the donkey. Again they passed by some people who pointed at the donkey carrying both Goha and his son.

"What a cruel man that is!" they said. "He has no pity for his donkey and allows both himself and his son to ride it at the same time."

Again Goha gave some thought to what the people had said, so he and his son got off the back of the donkey and both walked behind it. This time, passing by some people, he heard them saying among themselves:

"What a couple of fools those two are! Imagine walking when they have a donkey they could ride."

This time Goha was at a loss. Finally, after a lot of thought, he said to his son: "Come along then, let's carry the donkey between us."

So they lifted up the donkey and began carrying it along the road. As they were staggering along, some people saw them and burst out laughing.

"Look at those two madmen," they said, "carrying the donkey instead of riding on it!"

So they put the donkey down and Goha said to his son:

"You must know, my son, that whatever you do in this life, you will never please everyone."

GOHA AND THE THREE MONKS

Three wise monks came to the town where Goha lived. They asked the people there to introduce them to some of their own wise men so that they might ask them some questions.

So some men went off to Goha's house and asked him if he would meet these wise monks and answer their questions.

"And why not?" said Goha, and he put on his best clothes and his biggest turban. Then he saddled his donkey and set off to where the monks were waiting for him.

After Goha and the monks had exchanged greetings and all the people of the town were gathered round to see how their

friend Goha would answer the monks' questions, the first monk stood up.

"Where, wise Sheikh, is the middle of the world?"

Goha at once pointed his stick at the spot where his donkey had placed its left front foot.

"The exact middle of the world," he said, "is below where my donkey has placed its left front foot."

"And what proof do you have of that?" demanded the first monk.

"If you do not believe me," said Goha, "then dig down and see for yourself. If you find that I am wrong in what I have said, then you may call me a liar."

The three monks looked at each other and made no reply to this.

Then it was the turn of the second monk.

"How many stars," he asked, "are there in the sky?"

Goha at once answered: "As many as the hairs on my donkey."

"And how do you know that?" asked the second monk.

"If you do not believe me, then count the hairs on my donkey."

"And how can one count all the hairs on a donkey?" asked the three monks.

"And the stars in the sky," answered Goha, "are they to be counted?"

The three monks could find no reply to this.

And so it came to the turn of the third monk, who looked at Goha and asked:

"How many hairs are there in my beard?"

Without a moment's hesitation Goha replied: "The exact number as in my donkey's tail."

"And how can you prove that?" asked the monk.

"All you have to do," answered Goha, "is to go on pulling one hair from your beard and one hair from my donkey's tail. If it happens that in the end there are the same number of hairs in each, then I am right. If not, then I am wrong."

The three monks exchanged glances and burst into laughter.

"You have proved yourself a truly intelligent man, Sheikh Goha," they admitted. "How did you find such clever answers to our questions?"

Goha answered them: "If you are faced with a question to which there is no intelligent answer,
then any answer will do!"

GOHA AND THE PRINCE WHO WROTE POETRY

Goha was living in a country ruled by a powerful prince. This prince was a great general and had won many battles, but suddenly he decided that he would also like to become well known as a poet. Now Goha knew nothing about battles but he *did* know about poetry.

One day Goha was sitting in the palace when the prince read out a poem he had just written. Everyone, of course, said how beautiful the poem was. Everyone, that is, except for Goha, who remained silent.

"Did you not like my poem?" the prince asked Goha. Goha was still silent. The prince again asked Goha: "Did you not like my poem?"

This time Goha felt he must answer. "I would be lying, Your Majesty, if I said I liked it, and I do not like to lie to you."

The prince became angry and ordered his guards to lock Goha up in the royal stables for a night without food.

After this Goha rarely went to the palace. Then, one day, he went there and sat at the back of the room. For Goha's bad luck the prince had that morning written a new poem which he read out to those present. Immediately Goha rose to his feet and began to leave the room.

The prince noticed this and called out: "Where are you off to, Goha?"

"To the stable, Your Majesty," answered Goha. The prince laughed at Goha's reply and honoured him by inviting him to sit beside him.

GOHA AND THE BUTCHER

A man went into a butcher's shop and while the butcher's back was turned, he put his hand in a drawer and stole some coins. The butcher saw him out of the corner of his eye and said to him:

"You've stolen some of my money."

"Of course I haven't," said the man.

"I saw you," said the butcher. "I saw you put the money in your coat pocket." The man swore that the money he had was his own.

"Then you are coming with me to Goha the judge for him to decide which of us is lying," said the butcher.

The butcher took hold of the man and led him to the courthouse where Goha was sitting. Goha listened to what each of them had to say. He then asked for a bowl of hot water and ordered the man to drop into it the coins he had in his coat pocket. After a short time Goha could see some grease floating on the surface of the hot water.

"These are coins that the butcher has handled," said Goha. He gave the coins back to the butcher and sent the thief to prison.

GOHA AND THE COOKING POT

Goha had a neighbour who treated him as a fool. The neighbour used to borrow things from Goha and then find excuses for not returning them. Goha decided to teach his neighbour a lesson and to show him that he was not a fool.

So, one day, Goha asked his wife to go to their neighbour's house and ask to borrow a large cooking pot. She did this and the next morning Goha returned the pot with thanks. When his neighbour looked inside it he was surprised to find a much smaller pot there.

"What is this?" he asked Goha.

"My dear neighbour," Goha told him, "while your pot was in our house during the night it gave birth to this small pot. The small pot is, therefore, also yours."

The neighbour took both the pots from Goha, and told himself that he had been right to think that Goha was a fool.

Some days later, Goha again asked to borrow the large cooking pot. The neighbour immediately brought it.

When several days went by and Goha had not brought back the pot, his neighbour knocked on Goha's door and asked for it.

Goha bowed his head sadly. "Did you not hear, good neighbour? On the same evening that I borrowed your pot, I am sorry to say that it fell ill and died."

"Died?" shouted the neighbour. "Who has ever heard of a cooking pot dying? What rubbish are you talking?"

Goha looked at him straight in the eyes and said: "Would you not agree that a cooking pot that can give birth can also die?"

GOHA AND THE BRAYING DONKEY

Goha decided that he would like to go into business. So, when he heard that the donkey of a vegetable seller was for sale, he bought it.

Then, early each morning, he bought his vegetables from a farmer and made his way through the streets of the village with his donkey. As he went along he called out so that people would know what he was selling.

The donkey knew all the different houses whose owners used to buy vegetables. As the donkey approached each house it would give a loud bray. Goha tried to call out in praise of the vegetables he was selling but always his voice was drowned by the donkey's loud braying. Finally he threw down the rope and shouted at the donkey:

"Listen here, you - which of us is trying to sell the vegetables, you or I?"

48